Strong Spirit, Inspiring Tales

Lessons We Learn
from the Horses We Love

Strong Spirit, Inspiring Tales
©Product Concept Mfg., Inc.

Strong Spirit, Inspiring Tales
ISBN 978-0-9914172-1-6
Published by Product Concept Mfg., Inc.
2175 N. Academy Circle #200, Colorado Springs, CO 80909

©2014 Product Concept Mfg., Inc. All rights reserved.

Written and Compiled by Vicki J. Kuyper
in association with Product Concept Mfg., Inc.

All scripture quotations are from the King James version
of the Bible unless otherwise noted.

Scriptures taken from the Holy Bible,
New International Version®, NIV®.
Copyright © 1973, 1978, 1984 by Biblica, Inc.™
Used by permission of Zondervan.
All rights reserved worldwide.
www.zondervan.com

Sayings not having a credit listed are contributed by writers
for Product Concept Mfg., Inc. or in a rare case,
the author is unknown.

Strong Spirit, Inspiring Tales

*The wind of heaven is that which
blows between a horse's ears.*
Proverb

*B*eauty. Majesty. Courage. Camaraderie. Horses add so much to the world–and to our own individual lives. They also have so much to teach us; lessons that go deeper than simply "seize the moment" as you experience the joy of a carefree afternoon via horseback.

When you can't be in the saddle, travel through these pages. Let horses of all breeds and backgrounds, both misfits and record-breakers, lift your spirits and lead your heart toward insight and adventure.

Love

Diamond in the Rough

Pitch wasn't anyone's first pick. As blue roan's went, she was short, mean and ugly. She did her best to keep everyone–horses and people alike–at bay. Pitch spent most of the day in the far corner of her stall, trying to avoid contact with any living thing. When brought out into the open, she'd sit on the ground and paw like a dog.

The skittish mare wasn't named after her dark gray speckled coat, but for her ability to pitch anyone foolhardy enough to try and ride her. She'd dip down and then swoop upward to try and knock a rider in the dirt. If that didn't work, She'd head for a wall and try to force them, or frighten them, out of the saddle. No one wanted to ride her, let alone try and show her. Except for Lucy.

Lucy was a young girl who worked at the stables. In some ways, she kept to herself as well as Pitch did. Surrounded by the ranch's wealthy clientele, Lucy knew her place. It was grooming horses, not owning them. But Lucy's boss knew how much Lucy longed to have a horse of her own. So, he offered Lucy a deal: $300 for Pitch.

That amount of money wasn't to be taken lightly considering Lucy's tight budget. But she knew this might be her only chance at making her dream come true. So, despite Pitch's poor confirmation and ill-natured personality, she said, "Yes."

Pitch's gratitude was non-existent. Lucy wound up on the ground over and over again. Pitch would sit down and paw the dirt. If she chose to remain standing, she'd dip, swoop and bolt, anything to discourage Lucy from trying to gain any semblance of control. But Lucy didn't give up. Patiently, she spent all of her spare time trying to assure the horse that she was there for the long haul. That she wasn't going to hurt her. That she was going to earn her trust.

It took several months, but Pitch did begin to trust Lucy–as long as the horse could see her.

As soon as Lucy climbed up into the saddle, it was as though she had to start from scratch. Lucy continued talking softly, yet firmly, anytime she was around Pitch, whether in the saddle or off. One day, something clicked. Pitch made the connection between the loving girl who stood before her and the unseen rider on her back.

From that day on, Pitch seemed to undergo an entire personality change. Not only was she well-behaved, she held her head high, prancing proudly as though she were the most beautiful, talented horse in the ring. When Pitch and Lucy began competing, and winning, there wasn't any more talk about that "homely blue roan." Whenever Pitch and Lucy were together, some-how they both appeared to be more beautiful. Together, they brought out the best in each other.

Love has the power to transform us, people and horses alike. It sees our true potential and encourages us to live up to it. If we're hiding behind masks of insecurity, fear or pain, it helps us gain the courage we need to remove those masks. Then, we can risk change.

On our own, trying to break destructive habits and forge new, constructive ones can feel like an overwhelming task. But when those who love us commit to walk beside us, they help us get back up on our feet when we fall. If we're ready to give up, they remind us that failure is only a momentary setback. They help us see ourselves as God does, as creations worthy of love whose lives are filled with possibility and purpose.

*H*e hath made everything beautiful in his time.
Ecclesiastes 3:11

*G*od took a handful of southerly wind, blew his breath upon it, and created the horse.
Ancient Legend

*T*hough we travel the world over to find the beautiful, we must carry it with us or we find it not.
Ralph Waldo Emerson

*A*ll things bright and beautiful,
All creatures great and small,
All things wise and wonderful,
The Lord God made them all.
Cecil Frances Alexander

ATTITUDE

In the Mood

Horses are like a four-legged mood detector. They often mirror the emotions, attitudes and behavior of their riders. Angry rider? Feisty horse. Frightened rider? Skittish horse. Calm, confident rider? Strong, obedient horse.

Horses are emotionally intuitive animals. They pick up cues from a rider's tone of voice, breathing patterns and the posture of his or her body. Are you tense or relaxed? Your horse can tell the difference. Sometimes, they actually read us better than we can read ourselves–which is one reason why therapeutic riding programs are so successful.

Riding for physical and psychological benefits is nothing new. In ancient Greece, horseback riding was considered a valuable therapy for chronic illness. In the 17th century, riding was used to treat neurological disorders. But today's practice of therapeutic riding owes its widespread acceptance to one amazing woman: Lis Hartel.

In the 1952 Olympic Games, Danish equestrian Lis Hartel won the silver medal in dressage. That in itself is quite an accomplishment. But there's more to Lis's story. The Helsinki games marked the first time women were allowed to compete in equestrian show jumping and training events. Before then, only military men were allowed to compete, because Olympic equestrian events were considered too dangerous for women and civilians. (Even though women were already competing internationally in those same events outside the Olympics.)

But, winning the silver medal was just the first surprise Lis had in store for those in the stadium that day. When it came time for Lis to receive her medal, gold medal winner Henri St. Cyr from Sweden, carried her to the podium. That's because Lis was paralyzed from the knees down. Eight years earlier, at 23, Lis had contracted polio while she was pregnant with her second child. Unable to walk unaided, and with her arms and hands also mildly affected, doctors told the Danish national dressage champion that she would never ride again. But Lis, and her mare Jubilee, had other ideas.

Unable to use her legs, Lis guided Jubilee by gently shifting her weight in the saddle, using her back. Jubilee caught on quickly, seeming to understand, and adapt to, her rider's new limitations. There were plenty of falls and missteps along the way. But after three years of rehabilitation, Lis and Jubilee were able to compete in Scandinavian riding competitions. Lis followed her '52 Olympic medal with a silver in the '56 Olympics in Stockholm.

After her Olympic victories, Lis and her physical therapist founded Europe's first Therapeutic Riding Center. By the late 1960's equine therapy spread across the Atlantic, where the American Medical Association described it as "an invaluable therapeutic tool."

Today, therapeutic riding is not only used to improve the lives of people with physical disabilities, but emotional and behavioral challenges, as well. When horses respond to the emotions, attitudes and behaviors of their riders, those riders have the opportunity to become more self-aware. They gain a clearer picture of how they come across to the world on the outside–which is a reflection of what's going on inside. In turn, they learn to control their anger or fear, because they want to bond with their horse, to become better riders, trainers and all-around people. Riders learn to change their horses' actions, by learning to modify their own moods.

Winston Churchill said, "The outside of a horse is good for the inside of a man." Or woman. Horses aren't prejudiced or swayed by peer pressure. They don't judge you by what you can or can't do. They don't care what you look like or how much money you have. They don't harbor a hidden agenda. They respond positively to positive emotions and negatively to negative emotions. They "tell it like it is" in their own understated equine way.

Though people are more complicated than horses, they usually respond in a similar fashion. If you treat them positively, they'll respond in kind–and vice versa. So, take your emotional temperature every day. Pay attention to what you feel. Then, balance what you feel against what is real. Your moods matter. They make a difference in your day and in the day of those around you. Do your part in trying to make that day a more positive one.

There is nothing like a rattling ride for curing melancholy!

Winthrop Mackworth Praed

The greatest discovery of my generation is that man can alter his life simply by altering his attitude of mind.

William James

Could we change our attitude, we should not only see life differently, but life itself would come to be different. Life would undergo a change of appearance because we ourselves had undergone a change in attitude.

Katherine Mansfield

The greater part of our happiness or misery depends on our dispositions, and not upon our circumstances.

Martha Washington

HORSES PROVIDE THE
WINGS WE LACK.

LEADERSHIP

Taking the Lead

The evening thunderstorms dissolved into a perfect dawn. The handful of clouds remaining in the dusky sky turned a cotton candy pink, thanks to the first rays of the sun. Bart sat on his front porch, surveying the acres of farmland–his farmland–while nursing a warm mug of coffee in his still chilled hands.

Everything was so peaceful. Gertie, the dappled gray mare, nickered from her nearby enclosure, as if to bid her old friend, "Good morning!" Bart tipped his cup her direction, a toast to friendship and the promise of a brand new day.

The whine of an automobile engine sliced through the quiet. Both Bart and Gertie turned toward the unwelcome sound, just as the sleek blue convertible slid off the side of the muddy country road. It came to rest awkwardly in a ditch. Its tail lights were backed against Bart's split rail fence; its headlights pointed toward the rising sun. The engine sputtered, then was silent.

As quickly as his arthritic knees would allow, Bart rose from the comfort of his chair. By the time he'd made his way down the graveled path to the road, the driver was already out of his car, adjusting his tie and scratching his head.

Assured there was no permanent damage to his vehicle, or his mud-covered dress shoes, the stranger turned his attention to Bart. "Can you help me out, here?" he called.

"Yup," Bart replied. "I think Gertie and I can have you out of that ditch in no time."

The stranger quickly deduced that "no time" obviously meant something different to the farmer than it did to him. By the time Bart made it back to the car with his horse and a rope in tow, the man had already listened to his voice-mail, checked his email and texted his office, explaining he was going to be late to that out-of-town meeting he was headed to as soon as this farmer could turn his horse into a tow truck.

Bart hooked Gertie up under the front bumper of the little sports car. Then he yelled, "Pull, Dawson! Pull!" Gertie didn't move. "Come on, Old Blue...Pull! Give it all you've got!" The horse still didn't move. "You can do it Dusty! Pull! PULL!" Gertie continued to hold her ground. Then, Bart said softly, "Okay, Gertie, come on girl. Pull!"

With one great tug, the gray mare pulled the car back up onto the muddy roadway.

The businessman thanked the farmer profuse-ly. But before getting into his car, he turned to

Bart and said, "Okay, I have to ask. Why did you call the horse the wrong name three times?"

Bart said with a wizened smile, "Oh, that! Well, Gertie's as blind as a bat and kinda shy. If she thought she was the only one doing the job, she wouldn't even try!"

Are you a Gertie? If you doubt you have what it takes to be a leader, think again. Leaders come in all shapes, sizes, ages, temperaments…and breeds. Often the only difference between a leader and a follower is confidence. It takes courage to step up and accept responsibility. After all, the credit for a job well done, as well as blame for anything that goes wrong along the way, could both be yours.

But put credit and blame aside. Concentrate on building a winning team. Get to know your team well, honestly assessing their strengths and weakness. This includes yourself. Then, delegate wisely. Every unique member on a team has something he or she can learn and something he or she can teach the rest of the group. Your job is to bring out the best in each individual involved. Instead of viewing yourself as a leader, consider yourself the ultimate cheerleader. Then, raise your hand and volunteer to lead the way.

As is our confidence, so is our capacity.
William Hazlitt

Nobody holds a good opinion of a man who has a low opinion of himself.
Anthony Trollope

If seeds in the black earth can turn into such beautiful roses, what might not the heart of man become in its long journey toward the stars.
G. K. Chesterton

Confidence is that feeling by which the mind embarks in great and honorable courses with a sure hope and trust in itself.
Cicero

COMMON SENSE

Stubborn as a...

A love of horses often takes hold in child-hood. Young children picture themselves snuggling up to fuzzy palomino ponies or exploring grown-up freedom by riding off across the Sahara astride a fiery Arabian. Over time, those daydreams may change into sailing over jumps on sleek thoroughbreds in the Grand Prix or simply grooming a horse called "mine."

But in all of those equine dreams, most kids (as well as adults) give little thought to the horse's forgotten cousin, the mule. There are no

TV shows or movies heralding the bond shared between a young girl and her friendly Mammoth mule. It's true that mules are not the lithe, leggy darlings of the racetrack. Their long-ears are more reminiscent of a rabbit than a statuesque stallion. And then there's their temperament.

If mules do make their way onto the big or little screen, they are the surly sidekicks, portrayed as being as stubborn as a...well, a mule. But what is perceived as pigheadedness is in reality level-headedness—and intelligence. When it comes to brains, mules are known to be smarter than both of their parents: horses and donkeys. Research has shown that they are better at spatial relations, problem solving and making sound decisions based on safety and logic.

There's a good reason why a mule will refuse to ride in a calvary stampede or leap across a crevasse: It's not a wise decision. If a mule looks at a rickety bridge and conveys the message, "Nope. No way. Not me. Not now. Not ever!" by refusing to cross, it's best to listen. He's usually offering good advice.

Mules have played an important, though often overlooked, part in American history. The very first American mules are believed to have been bred by George Washington right after the Revolutionary War. Washington received an Andalusian jack (male donkey) aptly named "Royal Gift" from the King of Spain, which he crossed with his work mares. Mules helped plow fields, harvest crops and then transport that harvest to market–not only on Washington's farm, but later throughout the south.

During the Gold Rush, more than 31,000 mules were hard at work in northern California. A "Pack Mule Express" delivered mail to mining communities, then packed gold from the camps to the bank. As pioneers headed west, mules were often the "wagon train" animal of choice. Mules could pull wagons 30 miles a day, while horses and oxen only averaged five. Mules were also used by cavalry, infantry and artillery units as reliable pack animals in the Civil War and other military actions throughout the 1800s. Today, they're still the symbol of the U.S. Army. Mules helped build the Panama Canal and pull canal boats through the Erie Canal.

But perhaps the mules' biggest claim to fame in the U.S. was the role they played in transporting borax from Death Valley, California, to the nearest train station. Between 1883 and 1889, mules hauled over 20 million tons of "the miracle mineral" over the treacherous 165-mile trip. To accomplish this 20-day feat, two ten-mule teams were hitched together to form a 100-foot long, 20-mule team which pulled two 16-foot wagons of borax, as well as 1,200 gallons of water. Thanks to the mules' reliability, sure-footedness and sound judgement, not one mule was lost during those years.

If you're looking for a good friend, don't overlook the mule. They're not only smart, they're loyal. As long as you treat them right. But if you mistreat them, even once, you'll discover that "forgive and forget" isn't in their relational repertoire. Remember, mules aren't stubborn. They're sensible. A characteristic we could use a good dose of in our daily lives.

When it comes to finding a balance in life, we need to be part mule and part horse–to use both our head and our heart. To be fully aware of the risks we face, but sometimes risk everything for a worthy cause. To work hard and play hard. To hold onto faith and common sense. To acknowledge how we've been hurt, but learn to forgive. To love wisely, and well.

The three essentials to achieving anything
worthwhile are, first, hard work;
second, stick-to-itiveness; third, common sense.
Thomas Edison

Common sense ain't common.
Will Rogers

Common sense is seeing things as they are; and
doing things as they ought to be.
Harriet Beecher Stowe

Common sense is as rare as genius.
Ralph Waldo Emerson

WHEN YOU HAVE GIVEN
YOUR BEST TO THE DAY,
YOU CAN ENTER DAY'S END
WITH A MIND AT PEACE.

Reverence

The Call of the Wild

The year was 1909. Two riders entered an isolated camp in the Pecos Valley of New Mexico. The cowhands stopped branding cattle, uncertain whether or not to believe their eyes. One rider was seated astride a stately Arabian. The other rode a rather diminutive Shetland pony mix.

What was even more surprising than receiving visitors, a rarity in itself, was the age of the riders who'd entered their camp. Bud Abernathy, riding Sam Bass (the Arabian), was just 9-years-old. Temple, Bud's pony-riding brother, was only 5.

The men watched in amazement as Temple slid down Geronimo's leg and onto the ground. The boy's own legs were too short to dismount his pony any other way.

"What are you doing out here in nowhere?" one of the cowhands asked the boys.

Bud explained they were on the return leg of a journey from their home in Oklahoma to Santa Fe, New Mexico. The trip was 1,000 miles. Each way. The boys were making the journey with nothing but their horses, provisions, a firearm, a map, a checkbook, a New Testament wrapped in a silk scarf–and their father's blessing. The fact that their mother had died two years earlier came as no surprise to anyone who heard of their unescorted journey.

The boy's father, Jack Abernathy, had met up with the boys in New Mexico after the successful first half of their ride. The youngest U.S Marshal in American history, Jack accompanied his boys over the treacherous Glorieta Pass, keeping a keen eye out for robbers. Then he caught the train back home as the boys continued across country on horseback.

The cowhands warmly welcomed the boys into their unfurnished two-bedroom house. After treating the boys to a steak dinner, Bud and Temple slept soundly on the floor, using their saddles as pillows. In the morning, after a hearty breakfast, the men saw the boys off, following them for quite a distance to make certain they were safe.

When Jack made it home to Oklahoma, he received a letter written on a brown paper sack with a lead bullet. It was written by an outlaw named Arizona that he'd had a shoot-out with a few months before. Arizona voiced his dislike for Jack, but how much he liked his kids. He also told him how his gang had shadowed them through the toughest parts of New Mexico to make certain they were safe.

Two weeks after they left Santa Fe, the boys made it home. But that wasn't the end of their long distance rides. In 1910, President Theodore Roosevelt, a good friend of their father's, invited the boys to ride in a parade in his honor in New York City. So, Bud and Temple headed off to Manhattan. Unfortunately, Geronimo became ill along the way. He was shipped home by train and Big Black carried Temple the rest of the way.

As for the ride back to Oklahoma, the boys talked their father into buying a car and letting them drive it home. By themselves, of course.

But Bud and Temple's biggest challenge came when a man offered their father $10,000 if his sons couldn't ride across the U.S in less than 60 days. The journey from New York to San Francisco was both grueling and heartbreaking. Sam Bass died along the way. Both of the boys almost died, as well. Sixty-two days after leaving Manhattan, Bud and Temple arrived in San Francisco. They didn't win the bet, but their long-distance riding record has yet to be broken.

Whether you think Bud and Temple's adventures are parentally foolhardy or a unique method of teaching kids responsibility, you have to agree that heading off on horseback across country sounds like a tempting idea. There's just something about spending time in the saddle that spells freedom. Seeing the world go by from atop a four-legged friend invites us to bask in the beauty of creation and offer thanks to its Creator. Horses are more than loving, companions. They're a living, breathing invitation to be mindful of the things around us...and give reverence.

*R*iding a horse is not a gentle hobby, to be picked up and laid down like a game of Solitaire. It is a grand passion.

Ralph Waldo Emerson

A horse is a thing of beauty…none will tire of looking at him as long as he displays himself in his splendor.

Xenophon

*T*he wind of heaven is that which blows through a horse's ears.

Proverb

*S*pending that many hours in the saddle gave a man plenty of time to think. That's why so many cowboys fancied themselves Philosophers.

Charles M. Russell

*W*onder is the basis of worship.

Thomas Carlyle

Talent

Hidden Treasure

"She's gone, sir–disappeared!" the boy whispered to his boss. "The rest of the horses are all accounted for and every door is closed. I've no idea how she got out. Honestly, I think she's been stolen."

The grizzled, gray-haired man glared down at the young groom, knowing full well that as manager of the Blascovich stables in Hungary, he alone would be held responsible for the loss. Luckily, with more than 50 horses under his care, this particular liver chestnut filly had to be one of the least favored horses of the lot. True, she was a thoroughbred with impressive bloodlines. But she was also stick skinny, lop-eared and had a gut shaped like a pot-bellied stove. Her name, Kincsem (meaning "Treasure" in Hungarian), leaned more toward mockery than reality.

When the police traced the missing horse to a nearby gypsy camp, the first question the owner asked of the thief was, "Why that horse? If you were going to steal one, why not choose the best?"

The gypsy replied, "Because she'll be the greatest of them all."

Obviously, the owner wasn't convinced. When Kincsem ran her first race (in 1876), Ernest von Blascovich was noticeably absent. He missed seeing the ungainly filly cross the finish line twelve lengths ahead of the rest of the field. From that race on, Kincsem proved she was worthy of her name.

Kincsem loved to run. But that doesn't mean she did so with style. In a race in Budapest the following year, she refused to take her position at the starting gate. Her jockey threw up his hands in defeat and allowed her to continue grazing in a field adjoining the track. But after the rest of the pack began the race, Kincsem regained interest. She took off after them, grass still hanging out of her mouth, and headed down the track. She not only caught up with them, but passed them in what appeared to be an easy victory.

Awhile later in England, Kincsem competed for the Goodwood Cup against the Prince of Wale's famous thoroughbred, Pageant. Despite the thunderous roar of the capacity crowd as they cheered the start of the race, Kincsem fell asleep at the starting post. By the time she awoke, Pageant was far down the track with a healthy lead. True to form, that meant little to Kincsem. When she crossed the finish line, she was three lengths ahead of England's champion.

Kincsem won so consistently that bookmakers refused to give odds on her. When her career came to an end, she'd won 54 out of 54 races. Back home in Hungary, thousands of fans waited in line just to get a glimpse of their national "treasure." When she died in 1887, at the age of 14, Hungary officially went into mourning for three days. Flags hung at half-mast and Hungarian newspapers were edged in black in honor of her passing.

Kincsem's inelegant likeness has been recreated in statues around the world, from Kincsem Park in Budapest to the Santa Anita racetrack in Arcadia, California. To this day she is regarded as the most successful thoroughbred race horse in history. All because she did what she loved.

Kincsem had a gift. She could run. Fast. What talents do you possess? Can you sing? Paint? Whip up an amazing meal out of a fridge filled with leftovers? Fix a carburetor without glancing at the owner's manual?

Whatever comes naturally to you is a gift. And that gift is meant to be opened and enjoyed.

Putting your own unique gifts to use will not only give you pleasure, but often benefit those around you. It will also serve as a "thank you note" to the One who fashioned those unique talents in you before you were even born. So, follow in Kincsem's hoof prints. Show the world what a treasure you really are.

God has put something noble and good into every heart His hand created.
Mark Twain

The weakest among us has a gift, however seemingly trivial, which is peculiar to him, and which worthily used, will be a gift also to his race.
John Ruskin

Gypsy gold does not clink and glitter. It gleams in the sun and neighs in the dark.
Romani Proverb

Doing easily what others find difficult is talent; doing what is impossible for talent is genius.
Henri F. Amiel

Dogs look up to us.
Cats look down on us.
Horses look us straight
in the eye and see us as equals.

COURAGE

Duel in the Desert

Everyone just called him Spitty Spot. It wasn't his registered name. But the sorrel colt had a dark tobacco-colored splotch on its hip. Hence, his nickname. But the name wasn't given out of affection. Spitty Spot was a hard horse to catch, let alone ride. He was also easily spooked. If a summer breeze rolled a lone paper cup through the barn, he was the first to run.

But Cindy needed the money and working on the ranch was one way to earn it. She'd been hired to train horses, so she saddled up the one who needed it most: Spitty Spot. A few cows had gone AWOL overnight, so horse and rider headed out across the desert terrain of the ranch, determined to find them.

As usual, Cindy was also on the lookout for anything of interest she spied half-buried in the sand. She'd found all kinds of old treasure while on horseback. Today, that treasure was an antique purple bottle.

Usually Cindy wouldn't consider dismounting such an unreliable horse so far out in the desert, but the bottle warranted closer inspection. Cindy's boot had barely touched the ground when she saw something out of the corner of her eye—a snake ready to strike!

Fear overwhelmed common sense. Cindy dropped the reins and jumped backward to get out of the snake's striking range. In an instant, her mind projected two unpleasant scenarios: dying of a rattlesnake bite out in the middle of nowhere or dying of dehydration chasing a crazy colt over 285,000 acres of pasture.

As Cindy hit the ground, the colt struck out at the snake with its left foot, lightly grazing Cindy's jeans. Again and again he struck, a direct hit each time. Then, for his final blow, the colt pounced with both front feet like an Olympic diver hitting the springboard before executing a perfect double backflip.

Silence. Both horse and rider paused, then backed up a few steps before cautiously leaning forward to inspect their adversary. Together, they lowered their eyes…and saw a pulverized stick. If horses could roll their eyes, Cindy felt Spitty Spot would have joined her at that exact moment. Good thing horses are experts at keeping embarrassing secrets!

Cindy always had a little more respect for the sorrel after that. It wasn't in his nature to fight. It was in his nature to run. But for Cindy, he'd chosen "fight" over "flight" that day. Though Spitty Spot remained skittish and unreliable, Cindy knew there was more to him than met the eye. Spitty Spot had risen to the role of protector when it mattered most.

Fear is a funny thing. It can make people and animals act in unexpected ways. For better or for worse–regardless if what we fear is real or not!

The next time you feel fear start to build inside you, take a lesson from Cindy and Spitty Spot. Take a second look. What are you afraid of…really? Is your fear rational or fueled more by emotion than reason? Is fight or flight your wisest option?

If there's good reason to be afraid, pray for the courage you need to do what needs to be done. Then do it. The longer you put it off, the more your fear has a chance to grow. Even a "little fear," something as small as a "worry," can wiggle its way into every corner of your life by

making you feel anxious and uneasy throughout your day. Don't let fear diminish peace and
joy in your life. Face it. Analyze it. Deal with it.
Ask for help if you need it. Then give it a good
"stomp" and get on with your life.

*T*he horse is prepared against the day of battle: but safety is of the Lord.

Proverbs 21:31

*B*e strong and of good courage; be not afraid, neither be thou dismayed: for the Lord thy God is with thee whithersoever thou goest.

Joshua 1:9

*H*alf the things that people do not succeed in, are through fear of making the attempt.

James Northcote

*C*ourage is grace under pressure.

Ernest Hemmingway

*W*e gain strength, and courage, and confidence by each experience in which we really stop to look fear in the face…we must do that which we think we cannot.

Eleanor Roosevelt

Recognition

A Horse With No Name

"Wanted: Young, skinny, wiry fellows not over 18. Must be expert riders willing to risk death daily. Orphans preferred. Wages $25 per week." Eighty riders accepted the challenge of this newspaper ad in 1860. With the help of more than 400 horses, the Leavenworth & Pike's Peak Express Company was born.

The Pony Express (as it's more commonly known) was almost the Camel Express. In 1855, Congress set aside $30,000 to explore the feasibility of using camels for mail delivery between Texas and California. But logistically (and realistically!) horses won out as the most reliable precursor to modern-day mail delivery trucks.

The Pony Express route stretched from St. Joseph, Missouri to Sacramento, California–almost 2000 miles, which was covered in about 10 days. Seventy-five horses were needed to make a one-way trip, with a fresh horse needed every 10 to 15 miles. The breed of horse used depended on the terrain it would cover. Morgans and thoroughbreds were ridden primarily on the eastern side of the trail. Pintos were used in the mid-section. Mustangs were the horse-of-choice for the more rugged western end of the trail. Each horse cost up to $200, which was a high price to pay back in 1860.

The horses chosen for this grueling ride weren't technically "ponies," but their small, sturdy size inspired the Pony Express nickname. The average horse was 14 hands high, weighing about 900 pounds. Even the riders needed to be "pony-sized," weighing under 125 pounds.

On the difficult, fast-paced ride, every ounce mattered. When the Pony Express first began, the riders carried 20 pounds of mail, including letters, telegrams and special edition newspapers. Originally, the delivery cost was $5 per 1/2 ounce, but was soon reduced to $1 per ounce. Along with the mail and rider, each horse carried 20 pounds of gear, including a water sack, a Bible, two firearms and a horn used to alert the relay station master of a rider's arrival so he could ready the next horse and/or rider.

This exchange took less than two minutes. A leather saddlebag called a mochila was slipped off the horn of one horse's saddle onto the next. To save even more time along the trail, riders began carrying just the mail, a water sack and a revolver.

During a rider's shift (which lasted 75 to 100 miles), some were met along their route by wives and sweethearts bearing homemade treats. Tradition says one imaginative woman baked her cakes with a hole in them. That way her Pony

Express sweetheart could catch her treat on the barrel of his gun as he galloped by. Hence, the invention of the doughnut!

Nineteen months after the Pony Express began, the Pacific Telegraph Line was completed. Three days later, the Pony Express finished its last delivery. During its nineteen-month run, 34,753 pieces of mail were delivered and 308 runs were made each way. Although the route was hazardous, and at times deadly, only one bag of mail was ever lost. During its brief, but history-making operation, the brave horses and riders of the Pony Express carried the mail over 616,000 miles—equal to almost 25 trips around the earth.

The days of the Pony Express may be long gone, but the stories live on. Tales of riders like Charlie Miller (the youngest rider at only 11-years-old), or Jack Keetley (who rode 341 miles in 31 hours without eating or sleeping—if you don't count the fact that when he arrived at his relay station he was fast asleep on his horse!) or its most famous riders, Wild Bill Hickok and Buffalo Bill Cody. But there's something noticeably absent from almost all of these memorable tales. The names of the horses.

But that's the way it goes sometimes. When a team works together to accomplish a task, it's the goal, not individual glory, that matters. Horses never get their noses bent out of shape when they don't receive recognition for their valiant efforts. They do what needs to be done to the best of their ability. Period. Not bad advice, straight from the proverbial horse's mouth.

*D*on't be the rider who gallops all night and never sees the horse that is beneath him.
Rumi

*I*t is the art of mankind to polish the world, and everyone who works is scrubbing in some part.
Henry David Thoreau

*T*he reward for a thing well done is having done it.
Ralph Waldo Emerson

*T*he highest reward for man's toil is not what he gets for it, but what he becomes by it.
John Ruskin

BREAD MAY FEED MY BODY,
BUT MY HORSE FEEDS MY SOUL.

PROVERB

Joy

The Flying Horse

The next time you're in a theater anticipating the start of a great film, thank a horse. Sallie Gardner, to be precise. In the fall of 1875, the chestnut thoroughbred was on a roll. Her first recorded race was in September of that year, where she came in fourth. Over the next few weeks, and several races, Sallie held her own but never made her way to the head of the pack.

But on October 13th, Sallie's winning streak began. In four days the 3-year-old filly ran, and won, six races–totaling a distance of 6 1/2 miles. Little is known about Sallie's racing career after those amazing four days. But her real claim to fame came three years later.

Sallie's owner, Leland Stanford (a business-man, racehorse trainer/breeder and former governor of California), had long maintained that when a horse galloped there was a moment when all four hooves were simultaneously in the air. Back then, it was generally believed that horses were such massive creatures that they had to have some contact with the ground at all times. But in 1877, professional photographer Eadweard Muybridge attempted to prove Stanford's theory. He captured a moment of equine flight in a still photograph. However, Muybridge's negative appeared to have been retouched. So, naysayers considered the "proof" inconclusive.

Then, came Sallie. On June 19, 1878, on Stan-ford's farm in Palo Alto, California, Muybridge rigged 24 cameras along a track that ran parallel to where Sallie would run. The cameras' shutters were controlled by silk trip wires that were triggered by the horse's chest as she ran by at 36 mph. As the press watched, Sallie galloped, the shutters clicked and history was made. The series of photographs proved that horses can fly–even if just for a split second.

But when this series of photographs was run together in quick succession, they proved something else: that a series of still photographs could mimic action. "Sallie Gardner at a Gallop" became the first "motion picture." Subsequently, Muybridge invented the Zoopractiscope, a machine used to view his 24-frame animated film. Later on, Muybridge met with Thomas Edison who went on to develop the kinetoscope, which is a precursor to today's movie camera.

All Sallie did was what God created her to do. Gallop. But by doing so, she became part of something bigger, something that still has an impact on our lives today. Every individual life is its own unique "motion picture" played out in view of an ever-changing audience of friends and strangers. Some take part in the action. Some are merely spectators. Others may not be paying attention at all. However, that doesn't mean that what we do and say won't have an effect on them.

But, first and foremost the motion picture of our lives is a story we're telling, frame by frame, to ourselves.

We may believe that all we're really accomplishing in this life is running from here to there...taking care of details at work, doing our best to raise our children, ironing out relational wrinkles with family and friends, checking to make certain our coupons haven't expired, the recycling is on the curb before the trash truck arrives and our cholesterol is under control. But behind the scenes, perhaps going by so quickly that we don't even notice, are individual moments. Each one is a separate snapshot recording the choices we make. When played together in sequence, we see the true trajectory of our lives.

Are there times when you're flying? When your feet come completely off the ground? When you risk doing something just for the joy of it? Perhaps it's a foray into the arts, a time to play with paint or pottery, grab your camera or a musical instrument, sing and dance without worrying what others will think. Maybe it's going back to school to acquire what you need to head in a new direction, one your heart has always longed to go. It could even be making time in your schedule to not just read about horses, but spend time riding them–to fly on the back of a best friend.

Take time for joy. Moments when your heart can't help but soar are never wasted.

O! for a horse with wings!
William Shakespeare

*N*o hour of life is wasted that is spent in
the saddle.
Winston Churchill

*J*oy is peace dancing and peace is joy at rest.
Frederick Brotherton Meyer

*G*od forbid that I should go to any heaven
where there are no horses.
R. B. Cunninghame-Graham

AGE

The Gift of Years

"Just sell her," Russell told his father. "The horse is old. You're not going to get any more foals out of her. You hardly have enough money to feed yourself! All you do is feed her and clean up after her. What good is she to you at this point?"

Russell's elderly father absentmindedly ran his fingers through the few remaining strands of gray hair scattered across his head. He looked his son in the eye, then glanced down at the holes in his own well-worn shoes. "Your mother and I love her. That's reason enough."

When Russell left his parents' isolated country home that night, the good-byes were tense. Lars and Meg could barely look at each other, let alone at the weathered barn that housed Old Belle and the six other horses in their care. Lars and his wife of forty years were fully aware money was tight. They often settled for a small bowl of soup as their main meal, just so they could afford to care for their beloved charges.

Lars was so distracted by the unpleasant conversation with his son, he failed to notice the thin wisp of smoke that rose from the far end of the barn. But soon, the entire structure was aflame. By the time the smoke's acrid scent reached their bedroom, it was too late. The heat from the now raging fire was so intense Lars and Meg couldn't approach the barn doors to set their horses free.

Within the hour the fire department had come and gone, the fire was out and the barn lay in a towering heap of charred, smoking ruins. Lars and Meg, tightly clutching each other's hands, turned their backs on their heartbreak and headed up the gently sloping hill behind their home. At the top was a lone oak tree and a view of the entire valley. Their special spot.

As the stars twinkled in the ink black sky, the sound of their labored breathing broke the late night silence. But as they drew closer to the twisted branches of the old oak, they heard another sound. Breathing, but not their own. Then a nicker.

Lars' feet began to run at a speed they hadn't been accustomed to in years. His faint hope grew to full-blown joy. They were there, beneath the tree. Each and every beloved horse, including Old Belle.

Lars and Meg would never know the whole story, how Old Belle had been the first to notice the sparks that danced from the frayed wiring, the first to smell smoke–and the first to react. How she had worked the barn door open with her muzzle and pushed each horse toward the open air. How she had led the whole herd up the hill to safety and then waited patiently for the man and woman who'd lovingly cared for her since she was a spindly-legged colt.

Lars and Meg didn't need to know the whole story. All they needed was to know that their loved ones were safe. Old Belle included.

We may not like to admit it, but there may be people in our lives who we view the same way that Russell regarded Old Belle. Past their prime. No longer useful. Unlikely to make a significant contribution to the world around them—and to us. Even if we wouldn't be so bold as to suggest it was time they were "put out to pasture," we may minimize the incomparable value of those who are elderly or infirm. Those feelings may even carry over to the way we view ourselves as we grow older.

Every season of life has its beauty and its challenges. One priceless gift that comes with age is wisdom. Not everyone chooses to use it or share it with others. But if we do, we can continue to contribute to the world in a uniquely valuable way. So can those who've experienced more of this life than we have–if we choose to view age through new eyes, eyes open to see the wonder, promise and purpose in every day God's set before us.

*I*t would be a good thing if young people were wise and old people were strong, but God has arranged things better.

Martin Luther

*S*tand up in the presence of the aged, show respect for the elderly and revere your God.

Leviticus 19:32 NIV

*W*inter is on my head, but eternal spring is in my heart.

Victor Hugo

*I*t is not by the gray of the hair that one knows the age of the heart

Edward Bulwer-Lytton

*T*o be interested in the changing seasons is a happier state of mind than to be hopelessly in love with spring.

George Santayana

SOME OF MY BEST FRIENDS
        WEAR HORSESHOES.

FRIENDSHIP

Not-So-Odd Couples

What constitutes friendship? It's been said that what we look for in a friend is ourselves. While it's true that there's comfort in surrounding ourselves with people who see the world in a way similar to the way we do, there's also something to be said about "friending" outside the box. Take it from some extraordinary horses who've done just that.

Lots of horses develop playful relationships and close bonds with dogs who work on the ranches where they live. But there are also plenty of documented cases of cross-species relationships that stretch the limits of friendship even farther. Bonnie, a Morgan Quarter horse, began a friendship with a baby fawn when she rescued it from a coyote. We hear about horses like Champie and Streak who have especially close feline friends.

Then there's Jack and Charlie. At 24-years-old, Charlie was nearing the end of a horse's normal lifespan. So, when he started going blind, his owners considered putting him down. Then, Jack butted in and became his seeing-eye-goat.

Every day, Jack voluntarily led Charlie to his favorite pasture so he could graze. When Charlie eventually lost sight in both eyes, Jack began leading him from in front, instead of off to the side of his good eye. When leading Charlie through the forested property of the ranch, Jack never strayed from the path or stopped to have a snack along the way–which would be typical goat behavior. When Charlie got confused, Jack stopped and waited for his friend to catch up.

One day, a microburst left Charlie stranded in a grove of downed trees. Jack returned to the ranch house and bleated excitedly until the owners followed him to the spot where their blind horse was trapped. For sixteen years, Jack helped his friend Charlie in uniquely wonderful ways. When Charlie died at the age of 40, Jack's own health deteriorated rather quickly and he died soon afterwards.

Both Jack and Charlie lived exceptionally long lives for their respective species. But friendship has been known to have that affect. An Australian study followed 1,500 seniors for ten years. Researchers found that seniors who had the largest number of close friends outlived those with the smallest number by about 22 percent. They even found that having close relationships with adult children and other family members did not increase longevity as significantly as did having good friends. A Swedish survey of people 75 and older found also that those who kept in contact with a variety of friends had a lower risk of developing dementia.

But the health benefits of friendship aren't reserved for horses, goats and the elderly. Research has shown that breast cancer patients with ten or more close friends are four times less likely to die from the disease than those without a strong circle of friends. One possible explanation for this is that feeling lonely increases the production of the stress hormone cortisol in our brains. This can lead to increased blood pressure and hormonal imbalances, which can adversely affect our health.

Dare to expand your circle of friends beyond those who live in a stable. Volunteer. Get involved in your local church. Join a gym. Take a class. Strike up a conversation with your neighbors. Extend, and accept, invitations that encourage social connection.

Then, take a lesson from Charlie, Bonnie, Champie, Streak and others. Risk building friendships with those who may be outside your relational comfort zone. Those who are different from us can teach us things we never may have learned on our own. They can open our eyes to new points of view and perspectives. In the animal world, there are even predator and prey animals who have developed close bonds with those who might once have been considered dinner: like Anthony and Riley, a golden retriever and a cheetah at Tampa's Busch Gardens in Florida.

Who knows what the right friend can inspire, or tame, in you?

I heard a neigh. Oh, such a brisk and melodious neigh as that was! My very heart leaped with delight at the sound.

Nathaniel Hawthorne

*F*riendship multiplies blessings and minimizes misfortunes; it is a unique remedy against adversity, and it soothes the soul.

Baltasar Gracian

*T*here is nothing on earth more to be prized than true friendship.

Thomas Aquinas

*T*he only way to have a friend is to be one.

Ralph Waldo Emerson

*T*he firmest friendships have been formed in mutual adversity, as iron is most strongly united by the fiercest flame.

Charles Caleb Colton

SUCCESS

An Unlikely Hero

From a trainer's point of view, Black Jack was a failure. The coal-black gelding with the small white star was the "black sheep" of the U.S. Army. He threw riders to the ground at his training corral–over and over again. Not only wasn't he suitable for riding, Black Jack wouldn't pull anything and refused to parade. He was so ornery and uncooperative that he became a caparisoned horse by default.

The Morgan-American Quarter Horse cross was transferred from Fort Reno, Oklahoma, to Fort Myers, Virginia, home of the Caisson Platoon of The Old Guard. Dating back to 1784, The Old Guard is the Army's oldest active duty infantry regiment. The horses and soldiers stationed there participate in Armed Forces Full Honor funerals. Six horses pull the caisson, which transports the flag-draped casket, while the caparisoned horse follows behind.

This riderless horse represents the soldier who no longer rides with the brigade. The horse wears a cavalry saddle and sword. In its stirrups are backwards riding boots, symbolizing the end of a soldier's tenure. The caparisoned horse is accompanied by a handler who walks beside him throughout the solemn procession.

Sounds simple enough. But not for Black Jack. During his first stint as a caparisoned horse, Black Jack refused to just walk. He pranced, danced and threw his head. After the funeral, the army issued an apology to the family for Black Jack's behavior. But the family felt that the high-spirited nature of the horse reflected the irrepressible spirit of the loved one they were mourning. That was the beginning of a 24-year career.

Black Jack participated in over 1,000 military funerals. But none was more important than that of President John F. Kennedy. True to form, Black Jack was nervous, fidgety and prancing erratically through the two processions–one to the White House and one the next day to the Capital building. But he captured the heart of the American people, as well as that of the President's widow, Jacqueline. Two days after the funeral, she contacted the Secretary of the Army, requesting to buy Black Jack when he retired. Her request was granted.

Black Jack died at the age of 29. He was buried at Fort Myers with full military honors, only the 2nd horse in U.S. history to receive that honor. A monument was erected there, commemorating Black Jack's service–and the notoriety he gained throughout his "career."

There are plenty of human "Black Jacks" in this world. People whose lives don't quite follow the conventional road to success. But, success can't be measured by how our life looks on the outside. In the end, success is really an inside job.

Each one of us is a unique creation. Just like Black Jack. That means our potential is unique, as well. Where we were born, when and to whom, as well as our physical, mental and emotional make-up, are each individual puzzle pieces that when fit together construct a one-of-a-kind work of art called "me." Add firsthand experiences, personal choices and our own distinctive pilgrimage of faith and it becomes obvious that comparing the outcome of our journey to anyone else's is a waste of time. We can only compare who we are with who we were–and who we ultimately want to "grow up" to be.

How far have you come? And how far do you want to go? To answer these questions, you may need to redefine "success." Too often, the yardsticks we use to measure success (or failure) are fame and fortune. It's time to trade in that measuring stick for one of eternal value, one that considers invaluable qualities such as generosity, sacrifice, kindness and love.

There may never be a monument built to commemorate what you've accomplished in this life. But what you do for others carves a permanent mark in their lives, and therefore in history itself. Only you have the ability to touch people in your own singular way. Love others and be who God created you to be: that's the true key to success.

*W*e mount to heaven mostly on the ruins of our cherished schemes, finding our failures were successes.

Amos Bronson Alcott

*U*se what talents you possess: the woods would be very silent if no birds sang there except those that sang best.

Henry Van Dyke

*F*ar away there in the sunshine are my highest aspirations. I may not reach them, but I can look up and see their beauty, believe in them, and try to follow where they lead.

Louisa May Alcott

*S*uccess, which is something so simple in the end, is made up of thousands of things, we never fully know what.

Rainer Maria Rilke

*S*elf-trust is the first secret of success.

Ralph Waldo Emerson

IT IS NOT ENOUGH FOR A MAN
TO KNOW HOW TO RIDE;
HE MUST KNOW HOW TO FALL.

Proverb

FAITH

Witnessing the Impossible

Lynn wasn't one of the "rich kids," the ones who could compete in horse shows without considering the cost. She worked hard on the ranch to earn every dollar she needed to board her beloved grade mare, Nina. So, when 15-year-old Lynn and her even-tempered red sorrel qualified to compete with the high dollar horses at the Cow Palace in San Francisco, Lynn wasn't just excited. She was over the moon.

The morning of the show, it was still dark when Lynn and her mentor, Jan, loaded Nina into the trailer. Once all three of them were comfortably settled in, they began the ninety-minute drive south to the Bay Area. By the time they made it to the Golden Gate Bridge, the sun was just beginning to rise. The skyline of the city reflected back the first rays of dawn.

Traffic was light and everything seemed to be moving along right on schedule–until the trailer started hopping around like popcorn hitting hot oil! Lynn anxiously peered out the back window, fearing the trailer had fallen off the truck. The early morning light was still so dim, it was hard to make out anything that was going on behind the truck's cab.

But Lynn and Jan weren't the only ones who'd noticed something was wrong. Cars pulled up alongside them, passengers and drivers frantically waving their arms and pointing back toward the trailer that was continuing to jerk and lurch its way through traffic. But there's nowhere to stop or turn off on the bridge. So, for almost two miles, Jan continued navigating the narrow lane, while Lynn envisioned the worst. What if Nina had slipped and fallen in the trailer? What if her foot had wound up over the lead rope and she was choking? What if she'd caught her halter on a loose screw? The longer they drove, the more vividly Lynn envisioned blood and broken bones.

By the time they reached the other side of the bridge, Lynn was in tears. Having pulled into the closest turnout, both she and Jan ran to the back of the trailer and dropped the tailgate, expecting the worst.

There stood Nina, calm as a four-legged cucumber. Her lead rope was in place. Her hay was still in the feeder. Everything was secure. The only thing that seemed amiss was that her blanket was kicked off to the side. Lynn pulled Nina out of the trailer for a closer inspection. Other than a small nick above her eye, she was perfectly fine.

When Lynn went to put Nina's blanket back on, she noticed that the blanket wasn't ripped or torn in any way and that none of the straps had come undone. There's one thing both she and Jan were sure of: when a horse is tied in a horse trailer it's impossible for it to remove its blanket without removing any straps.

Or is it?

Perhaps it should have been impossible for a 15-year-old girl from the wrong side of the financial tracks to win two second place ribbons at the Cow Palace, and take home the blue ribbon in her equitation class. But it happened.

From little things (like how a mare pulls a horse-blanket Houdini while secured in a trailer) to big things (like how a baby is born), life is filled with the wonderful, the inexplicable and the seemingly impossible.

When we stop long enough to pay attention to the world around us, we recognize that what's often considered ordinary is actually extraordinary: how every fourth generation of Monarch butterfly migrates to the same location without ever having been there before; how we are "standing still" on a planet rotating over 1000 miles an hour; how our bodies can live for decades, existing on a bit of oxygen, food and water.

Matthew 19:26 says that "With God all things are possible." When we hold onto that truth, we realize that "impossible" is simply a synonym for "beyond our understanding." That's what faith is all about—moving forward with confidence, without having to know all the answers, because we have faith that God does.

*B*elief is a truth held in the mind. Faith is a fire in the heart.

Joseph Fort Newton

*H*e that will believe only what he can fully comprehend, must have a very long head or a very short creed.

Charles Caleb Colton

*G*od moves in a mysterious way
His wonders to perform;
He plants His footsteps in the sea,
And rides upon the storm.

William Cowper

*L*ife is the art of drawing sufficient conclusions from insufficient premises.

Samuel Butler

COMMUNITY

The Hands That Help

It was almost Christmas. Several blizzards had already barreled through this isolated valley of the Canadian Rockies, leaving behind six feet of snow. This morning, a light flurry added to the icy blanket, bowing the branches of the evergreens that reached up the mountain slopes.

Even though the temperatures were well below zero, two men mounted their snowmobiles. But today wasn't about adventure. It was about search and rescue. Luckily, the less experienced snowmobilers who'd abandoned their sleds on the mountain a few days before had been rescued. Now, it was time to do the same for their vehicles.

As the men searched for the sleds, they noticed what they thought were moose just above the treeline. As they drew closer, the men realized their "moose" were actually horses. Listless and emaciated, the two horses huddled together in a tight enclosure of snow they had packed down around them. The men were prepared to rescue sleds, but horses? Civilization was over 20 miles away. With snow this deep, and the horses this close to death, was there any way to save them?

The snowmobilers knew they couldn't rescue these horses without help. But that's the beauty of living in community. Help is always close at hand. And when everyone harnesses their creativity, energy and unique gifts together to work as a team, they can do what seems impossible. But first, the call for help had to spread.

The next day, two became four. And the next, four became eight. The rescue team brought blankets to cover the horses and carefully fed them small amounts of hay, so their digestive tracts (on the brink of starvation) wouldn't seize up. They melted snow to provide the horses with water. Then, they began the tedious job of digging a trench through the wall of snow and ice from the horses to a logging road over a half mile away. But the going was slow. Too slow if the horses had any hope for survival. A full day's work only yielded a few dozen yards of progress. Then, their rescue efforts were picked up by national TV.

Two days before Christmas–with temperatures reaching 40 degrees below zero–farmers, ranchers, oil rig workers, snowmobilers and ordinary "mountain folk" came together to dig a road to freedom for the 3-year-old bay mare and the 14-year-old sorrel gelding. By 1:30 that afternoon, the trench was completed. An hour later, the horses had made it to the road. The next challenge was the 18-mile walk to the parking lot where a rancher with a stock trailer could transport them to their new home. At 10 pm that evening, they were on their way.

Only the two pack horses abandoned by an ill-equipped owner three full months before their rescue, know the full extent of their battle for survival. But despite their valiant partnership, they could not have made it on their own. They were forced to rely on the kindness of strangers. Sometimes, we may find ourselves in that position, too.

It's been said that it takes a village to raise a child. But our need for a village doesn't end with adolescence. Throughout our lives we need the wisdom, companionship and aid of those around us. Our village includes neighbors, friends and family. But it may also extend to those we regard as strangers. Doctors, counselors, social workers, as well as the staff of local churches and charities are ready to help. But like

the snowmobilers who were determined
to rescue Belle and Sundance, we need to be
vocal enough, and humble enough, to make our
needs known.

When you need a helping hand, call on your
village–and don't forget to return the favor when
your village calls on you.

The race of mankind would perish did they cease to aid each other. We cannot exist without mutual help. All therefore that need aid have a right to ask it from their fellow man.

Sir Walter Scott

To live in society doesn't mean simply living side by side with others in a more or less close cohesion; it means living through one another and for one another.

Paul-Eugène Roy

A community is like a ship; everyone ought to be prepared to take the helm.

Henrik Ibsen

There is a destiny that makes us brothers:
None goes his way alone;
All that we send into the lives of others
Comes back into our own.

Edwin Markham

God divided man into men, that they might help each other.

Seneca

NOT A FANCY STABLE,
BUT LOVING CARE,
MAKES FOR A HAPPY HORSE.

TRUST

Face Off

The white-tailed deer was on the losing end of the race. Despite its speed and agility, it was no match for a 700 pound grizzly bear–until it ran into a massive white draft horse leading a trail ride. The deer burst from the forest thicket, grazed Tonk's left front shoulder, then made a sharp turn. The bear kept lumbering straight ahead. It no longer had the deer in its sights. Its focus had shifted to a horse named Scout, with an 8-year-old boy clinging desperately to the horn of his saddle.

Scout took off up an incline, while the rest of the panicked horses fled back down the trail toward the barn. Well, all the horses except for Tonk. At eighteen hands high, Tonk stood out from the other trail horses like a Trojan horse among ponies. Best as anyone could tell, his lineage included quarter horse and Percheron. But, Tonk's skittish disposition leaned more toward flight than fight. Yet the young wrangler who'd ridden Tonk for the last few months knew that today, flight was not an option for either of them. Today, their responsibility was to the inexperienced rider mounted on Scout.

Tonk's natural inclination was to join the rest of the pack in their mad dash to the barn. But his rider, dug her heels into his side. Out of trust and obedience, Tonk responded. He ran straight into the path of the oncoming bear, cutting the grizzly off from Scout and the boy. Snarling at Tonk's interference in the chase, the bear charged Tonk. Going against both instinct and common sense, Tonk followed his rider's command and charged the bear.

Like two jousting knights, the bear and the horse ran straight toward each other. Within 10 feet of an ursine and equine collision, the bear swerved. But the grizzly wasn't about to turn tail and run. He dodged Tonk and ran back toward Scout–and the boy who'd just fallen off this mount into a tall patch of wild grass.

Once again, Tonk obeyed the wrangler and charged the bear. This time, the grizzly admitted defeat and ran off into the trees. The wrangler helped the frightened boy up onto Tonk's saddle along with her, grabbed Scout's lead and headed off to find the other riders.

It took a full ten minutes before the group was reunited; the boy and his father enjoying the sweetest reunion of all. But another bond was forged deeply that day, a bond between Tonk and the wrangler. When the summer season drew to a close, the wrangler refused to let Tonk head back home with the other leased horses. His home would now be with her. She knew that any horse willing to risk his life to follow her command was a horse worthy of her utmost love and trust.

Trust grows when it's put to the test. Despite Tonk's size, he was really no match for an angry grizzly. It was Tonk's trust in the wrangler, and the wrangler's trust in him, that made them an unbeatable pair. Who do you trust…and why?

Whether it's trusting your best friend to keep something you've said in confidence, trusting your child to walk to the store on his own for the very first time or trusting that God will give you the strength you need to get through a major storm in your life, trust involves risk. That means it's going to be uncomfortable at times.

But the more those around you prove themselves trustworthy in little things, the easier it will become to trust them with big things.

*T*reat people as if they were what they ought to be, and you help them become what they are capable of being.

Johann von Goethe

I will say of the Lord, He is my refuge and my fortress: my God; in him will I trust.

Psalm 91:2

*F*ew things help an individual more than to place responsibility on him and to let him know that you trust him.

Booker T. Washington

*A*ll I have seen teaches me to trust the Creator for all I have not seen.

Ralph Waldo Emerson

Self-Worth

Two of a Kind

Drifty wasn't my first horse. And I know you're not supposed to say it (especially if you've been fortunate enough to have loved a long line of wonderful horses in your lifetime), but she was always my favorite. She was the first horse I purchased with my own money. The first I raised from a weanling. My first taste of true love.

I'd worked at the stables since I was twelve. At the age of 17, I'd been around horses long enough to understand the hard work, commitment and expense that comes along with owning a horse of your own. But I was ready for a new challenge. When I chanced upon the liquidation sale catalog from a local quarter horse breeder, I remember thinking, This is it! I'll buy a new horse and start from scratch.

Of course, choosing the right horse isn't a decision to be taken lightly. I studied the catalog page by page, highlighting possible companions. I really wanted a filly, so right off the bat I rejected any of the stud colts. I underlined favorite bloodlines and traits that I thought would be a good match with my own temperament and experience.

Once my homework was done, I drove to the ranch to check out the possibilities in person. For me, walking into the pen filled with beautiful weanling fillies was like walking into the ultimate candy store! I carefully watched each baby as he or she trotted by, checking out their hip number and comparing it with the catalog. My first choice was a beautiful chestnut filly with flaxen mane and tail. On paper she was perfect. But in person, she seemed skittish and distracted. We simply didn't connect, so I marked her off the list. I rejected a few others I'd dog-eared as "perfect" in my catalog, as well.

Then I saw Drifty. She was a big bay filly with not one white hair. She was calm and easygoing, a joy to be with. As she trotted around the corral, she was the picture of beauty and grace. In my head and my heart, I'd made my choice. But being young, and uncertain of the wisdom of selection, I thought I'd stay awhile and watch everyone else look through the herd.

Buyer after buyer walked in the pen and passed Drifty right by. What was wrong? She had wonderful bloodlines, a sweet disposition, good confirmation and a beautiful gait. But not one person gave her more than a passing glance. After awhile, I got up the courage to ask someone what they thought of the big bay filly, Number 143.

"There's nothing really wrong with her," the man replied. "She's just nothing special. She's plain, that's all."

Plain. I certainly didn't see her that way. In fact, it never crossed my mind that she wasn't as flashy as the other horses in the pen. But in looking around at all of the other colts with the big blaze faces, flashy white socks and beautiful flaxen manes, I understood what he meant. And it made me want her even more. She was being undervalued, overlooked, and under appreciated simply because she was a bit plain…just like me.

A week later, she was mine.

Drifty and I were together for years. She got me through my awkward twenties, including a devastating divorce. I stuck with her when she injured her leg right before the Snaffle Bit Futurity Open Championship. And later, when she lost her foal. We were a team.

We had almost 20 years together. We matured together, learned together and gained confidence together. She was an extraordinary mare. And over the years she opened my eyes to an invaluable truth: that she was smart, hard-working, talented and dependable…just like me.

*S*how me your horse and I will tell you what you are.

Proverb

*N*o one can make you feel inferior without your consent.

Eleanor Roosevelt

*A*ll men are ordinary men: the extraordinary men are those who know it.

G. K. Chesterton

*E*very individual has a place to fill in the world, and is important, in some respect, whether he chooses to be so or not.

Nathaniel Hawthorne

KEEP CALM
AND RIDE ON.

PERSEVERANCE

The Impossible Journey

Despite the relentless rain, a crowd gathered to watch their departure. It wasn't admiration or celebration that drew the press and a smattering of onlookers to this square in Buenos Aires on April 24, 1925. It was disbelief.

The two Criollo horses and their red-haired human companion were curiosities. Mancha (The Spotted One) and Gato (The Cat) were still half-wild, known for their ornery tempers, as well as their intelligence and stamina. Descen-

dants of the horses brought to South America by
the Spanish conquistadors, the sturdy geldings
were more accustomed to running free in the Ar-
gentine pampas than sporting saddles in the big
city. When offered oats or alfalfa to eat, they preferred their straw bedding. Their recent "domesti-
cation" was tentative, at best. At least their lineage
earned them the respect of the local onlookers.

The same couldn't be said for their companion, Aimé Félix Tschiffely. Born in Switzerland,
the transplanted 30-year-old school teacher was
an inexperienced rider with a deep-seated hunger for adventure. His plan? Ride from Buenos
Aires to Washington, D.C.. The fact that a young
stable boy rode beside Tschiffely in the rain that
first morning, to help lead the unlikely trio out of
town, didn't bode well for the remaining 10,000
miles of their journey. But Tschiffely, and his
horses, had tenacity on their side. They'd need it.

For the next three years, they traveled through
jungles and swamps, across raging rivers and
quicksand bogs, over the Andes mountains and
across the Matacaballo ("Horse-killer") Desert.
During their grueling ordeal, an unbreakable

bond of trust and friendship was formed. At nightfall, Mancha and Gato didn't need to be tied. They never ventured far from their master's side.

They trusted Tschiffely enough to follow him over rickety rope bridges, some of which were so treacherous that grown men had to be blindfolded or tied onto stretchers to make it across. They faced blistering heat, vampire bats and summits so high they made Tschiffely's nose bleed. But together, they survived them all.

Their arrival in the United States was met with much more fanfare than their inauspicious departure three years earlier. After meeting with President Calvin Coolidge, speaking at the National Geographic Society and receiving a medal of honor from the mayor of New York City, Tschiffely booked three tickets home to Argentina onboard the Vestris. Luckily, Tschiffely, Mancha and Gato missed the boat. It sank during the voyage, resulting in the loss of 110 lives. A few weeks later, the trio boarded the Pan American for their successful 28-day voyage home. Today in Argentina, the National Day of the Horse is celebrated each year in recognition of Mancha, Gato and Tschiffely in recognition of what was initially regarded as an impossible journey.

There will be journeys each one of us faces that may seem impossible on Day One. Journeys that may not be anticipated with pleasure or excitement. Journeys we don't choose. But we need to face them the same way Tschiffely, Mancha and Gato faced the 10,000 miles ahead of them—one step at a time.

Whether the "impossible" journey we face is financial, relational, emotional or physical, it's important to look realistically at the big picture. But it can be overwhelming, and discouraging, to continue to focus on it for long periods of time. Once we get our bearings, it's time to concentrate on what's right in front of us, the first step we need to take.

Like Tschiffely, before we make it to NYC, we first need to make it out of Buenos Aires! Today, what will you do? How will you move forward? The secret to perseverance may be hard, but it isn't complicated. It's taking one day, one hour, or even one minute at a time. So get up and get going. There's no time like the present to mount your horse and ride.

A good horse makes short miles.
George Eliot

*B*y perseverance the snail reached the ark.
Charles Haddon Spurgeon

*P*erseverance is the sister of patience, the daughter of constancy, the friend of peace, the cementer of friendships, the bond of harmony and the bulwark of holiness.
Bernard of Clairvaux

*P*erseverance is not a long race; it is many short races one after another.
Walter Elliott

I recommend you to take care of the minutes, for the hours will take care of themselves.
Philip Dormer Stanhope

CONTENTMENT

Plan B

A lot of teenage girls want a horse of their own. Lisa was no exception. But, like a lot of parents of teenage girls who want a horse, Lisa's parents had to say "no." But that didn't stop Lisa. She decided to make the best of what she had. And what she had was a dairy cow named Chocolate Bar.

Shortly after the milk chocolate brown dairy cow was born on her family farm, Lisa put a halter on the calf and started taking her on daily walks through the countryside near where her family lived. As Chocolate Bar grew more accustomed to human companionship, Lisa helped acquaint her bovine companion with an old, used saddle. In six months time, Lisa took the next logical step: she hopped on her cow and went for a ride. Well, for a couple of yards, anyway.

But, Lisa was determined–and armed with a good deal of patience, sugar and carrots. Over time, Chocolate Bar warmed to the idea of carrying Lisa on hour-long rides through the forest. Yet Lisa didn't stop there. Lisa didn't just want to ride, she wanted to jump! That meant more training, cajoling, caressing, treats and time together. While not quite as enthusiastic as "the cow that jumped over the moon," Chocolate Bar did learn to jump over two to three foot high hurdles.

Lisa and Chocolate Bar spent countless afternoons, riding, jumping and just hanging out together. So much so, that other members of

Chocolate Bar's herd began shunning the cow. Chocolate Bar tried hanging out with the horses, but they didn't really care for her hanging around either.

So, the cow that wanted to be a horse, loved by the girl who wanted a horse but reset her sights on a cow, developed their own special bond. One that never would have happened if Lisa and Chocolate Bar had refused to think outside the proverbial box.

There will be plenty of times in our lives when what we want doesn't line up with what we get. Sometimes, what we view as a "no" answer to a heartfelt prayer is a nudge to push us in a new direction. That direction may be challenging. It may not look anything like the picture for our future we had in mind. But it may also lead us toward blessings, and relationships, we would have never experienced if life had gone the way we'd originally envisioned it would.

Where happiness is concerned, contentment is the key that unlocks its most priceless treasures. It's easy to be content when everything is going our way. But contentment is also within reach when life throws us a curve ball. It comes from learning to adapt to the unexpected. As we focus on what we have, instead of what we believe we lack, our perspective will begin to shift. We'll discover beauty in unpredictable places. Strength and courage we didn't know we had. Opportunities hiding in the shadows. Gifts and talents waiting to be refined. God's hand working for us, not against us.

This doesn't mean resigning ourselves to the way things are or choosing to settle for second best. It means we're embracing reality with open arms. The time we've been given on this earth is relatively short. Whether it will be sweet, largely depends on us and our attitude. Yes, that can mean that when life gives us lemons we learn to make lemonade. It can also mean that when life hands us a cow, we learn to ride it with our head held high.

I have learned to be content whatever the circumstances. I know what it is to be in need, and I know what it is to have plenty. I have learned the secret of being content in any and every situation, whether well fed or hungry, whether living in plenty or in want.

Philippians 4:11-12 NIV

*I*t is right to be contented with what we have, never with what we are.

James Mackintosh

*T*he discontented man finds no easy chair.

Benjamin Franklin

*H*e who is not contented with little will never be satisfied with much.

Thomas Benton Brooks

HE RIDES AT EASE WHOM THE
GRACE OF GOD CARRIES.

THOMAS À KEMPIS

Loss

Bittersweet Blessings

When it comes to celebrity, there's one horse in India that rises head and tail above the rest: Chetak, the Marwari warhorse. Numerous songs and stories commemorate his valor. Racehorses continue to be named in his honor. But they're not all that bears his name. "Chetak" is also an express train line, a children's game, a horse fair, a shopping area and a popular brand of motor scooter. There's even one day of the year dedicated to recognizing Chetak's contribution to the survival of India's Rajputs, or "warrior clan."

Marwaris are one of five breeds of horses indigenous to India. Like their Indian "cousins" the Khathiawari, their ears curl upward, meeting at the top of their head to form an arch. These distinctive ears are more than decorative. They can swivel 180 degrees, providing exceptional hearing. Views vary on how the Marwari breed began. Some say they're one of the few ancient breeds of horse still alive today. Others believe that in the 12th century the Rajputs interbred Arabians, Turkumans and other local stock to create a sturdy, fearless breed known for its loyalty and intelligence. Still others believe that the Marwaris have been around since the creation of the earth, when, in their legends "horses had wings."

Chetak didn't have wings. But he did have a trunk. At least, he did on the battlefield. When Mogul warriors attacked the kingdom of Marwar, they rode elephants into battle. To fight back, the Rajputs fashioned false trunks that their horses' wore over their muzzles. This tricked the elephants into thinking the horses were baby elephants—which they wouldn't attack. When a Marwari approached an elephant, it would rear up on its back hooves and put its front feet on the elephant's head. This allowed Rajput warriors to more easily fight their foes.

Chetak wasn't just any Marwari with a trunk. He was the beloved stallion of the royal Rajput leader, Maharana Pratap. Both were known to be fearless in battle. But even their courage and skill weren't enough to turn the tide of the battle of Haldighati. On June 21, 1576, 20,000 Rajput warriors on Marwaris faced 80,000 Moguls on elephant-back. The battle lasted only four hours.

The Maharana tried to stop the Moguls' advance by attacking the emperor of the Moguls. Chetak reared high in the air and placed his front hooves on the forehead of the elephant of the Mogul's imperial commander. The Maharana attacked, but his efforts were only partially successful. For Chetak, however, they ultimately proved fatal. Yet even with one hind leg severely injured by an elephant tusk, Chetak carried his master over two miles to safety. After jumping a small stream, Chetak collapsed and died in his master's arms.

The Maharana was grief-stricken over his courageous companion and fellow warrior. He promised to never forget the the sacrifice Chetak had made for him and the Rajput clan. Several years later, the Maharana built a monument on that same spot by the river where Chetak had died, commemorating his horse's unparalleled bravery, loyalty and sacrifice. That monument is still standing today.

Great love carries a potentially painful flip side: great loss. Whether the ones we love walked around on two legs, or four, figuring out how to keep moving forward without them isn't easy. The more we love, the more we have to lose. But the risk is worth the reward. The joy of love is worth the pain of loss.

Mourning is only part of the grieving process. Celebrating those we've been blessed enough to hold in our arms, and our hearts–even for a short time–is another. The freedom to whole-heartedly celebrate those we've lost may not come quickly or easily. It may always feel a bit bittersweet. But the joy the ones we love bring into our lives doesn't end with death. Every memory we made together, every way they changed our lives for the better, makes every subsequent day better. That includes today.

I will turn their mourning into joy, and will comfort them, and make them rejoice from their sorrow.

Jeremiah 31:13

*N*othing can make up for the absence of someone whom we love, and it would be wrong to try and find a substitute. It is nonsense to say that God fills the gap; God doesn't fill it, but on the contrary, keeps it empty and so helps us to keep alive our former communion with each other, even at the cost of pain

Dietrich Bonhoeffer

*G*ive sorrow words: the grief that does not speak whispers the o'er-fraught heart, and bids it break.

William Shakespeare

*T*here are times when God asks nothing of his children except silence, patience, and tears.

Charles S. Robinson

Second Chances

Lucky Break

When Duke wouldn't come to the gate, I knew something was wrong. Nothing would keep him from his breakfast. When I called his name, he lifted his eyes to meet mine. But he remained where he was, backed into the corner of his stall.

"What's wrong, fella?" I asked. Pulling a carrot out of my coat pocket, I tried to tempt the exquisite bay stallion into coming to greet me, but he still didn't move. So I went in to greet him.

After all, Duke was more than my friend. He was also a rather weighty investment. A Danish Warmblood, Duke was bred for competition. Kind of like me. We'd been together less than a year, but I had high hopes for a long, winning, future together. That is, until I saw how he was favoring his left front leg.

Luckily, a very well-respected large animal vet resided nearby, so I gave him a call. After looking over Duke, and x-rays of his leg, he announced his diagnosis: no break. Nothing wrong at all.

Relieved, I chalked it up to Duke having a bad day. But the next day, he wasn't any better. He was still hopping. I didn't know whether horses could suffer psychosomatic illnesses like people, but one thing was for sure, Duke seemed to be suffering. I tried comforting him, challenging him, encouraging him. Nothing seemed to help. So, I decided simply to show him how much I cared. I pampered him. I hung hay up in his stall so he could eat easily. Then, I called on my close community of fellow horse lovers.

As a group, we lavished love and care on my beautiful bay. We each signed up for shifts as "caregiver." For 24 hours a day, someone would enter Duke's stall every two minutes. What we offered seemed so small…we'd talk to him, stroke him, give him a bite or two of an apple. Anything to take his mind off of the pain.

Eight weeks later Duke put his foot down. Literally. The morning he walked across his stall to greet me felt like as much of a triumph as winning first place in dressage. Later that week, the vet and I happened to cross paths in the grocery store. I told him what had happened since I'd seen him last. Curious, he asked if he could take another look at Duke. After examining Duke, and a new set of x-rays, the vet asked if he could meet with me in private.

"I am so sorry," he said to me, his eyes filling with tears. "It appears Duke had a horrible break in his leg. I don't know how I missed it in the first set of x-rays. But in the second, I can see how that break has completely healed. The truth is, if I'd caught it earlier, I would have been adamant about putting him down. But look what you've done! Your love, and my mistake, has given him a second chance at life."

Duke went on to become the winner I knew he was born to be. He's also become a touchstone in my life. He's living proof that mistakes are not always bad. Sometimes, they can even change our lives for the better.

Second chances are not synonymous with second best. They're a gift. A fresh start. If a mistake, either mine or someone else's, leads me down a different path than the one I've envisioned for my day–or my life–I try to view it as an unanticipated adventure. Not every moment of an adventure is guaranteed to be easy or pleasant. But one thing is certain, every adventure's an opportunity to explore a new set of options. I can't change the past. But every day provides an open invitation for changing the future.

*W*e are troubled on every side, yet not dis-
tressed; we are perplexed, but not in despair.
2 Corinthians 4:8

*O*n the occasion of every accident that befalls
you...inquire what power you have for turning
it to use.
Epictetus

*T*here are no accidents so unlucky from which
clever people are not able to reap some advan-
tage, and none so lucky that the foolish are not
able to turn them to their own disadvantage.
François de La Rochefoucauld

*T*roubles are often the tools by which God fash-
ions us for better things.
Henry Ward Beecher

EXPECTATIONS

Dream On

Lacey eyed the money in her hand. It was all she had. Every last cent. But she knew that the opportunity to ride a horse would be worth it all. She'd ridden horses in her dreams, of course. She'd raced a stallion black as a moonless night across miles of open plains, trotted a pinto pony over grassy knolls dotted with wildflowers, even held her breath at the starting gate as the thoroughbred beneath her strained to be set free, ready to gallop around the track in record-breaking time. But today would be the very first time her dreams would come true.

The horse that stood before her now wasn't the most beautiful she'd ever seen. Its dull chestnut coat almost matched its lackluster brown eyes. It stood motionless. Certainly this wasn't his first ride. But Lacey wasn't disheartened. Her heart beat as wildly as it had in her dreams.

I think I'll call him Thunderbolt, she said to herself, uncertain of any other name he might already have been given.

Lacey pulled herself up into the saddle with ease, as if she'd been doing it for years. Perched proudly atop Thunderbolt, she felt as regal as a church steeple. Then, the horse began to move.

It seemed gentle, at first. A soft, rhythmic sway. But then Lacey began to bounce in the saddle like a small rubber ball. Lacey squeezed Thunderbolt's sides with her legs to try and remain steady, but she felt herself slipping to the side. She gripped the reins, trying desperately to hang on. It was no use. Seconds later, Lacey's head was pointed downward and the ground was coming up fast. Though Lacey continued to slide, her right foot was held fast in the stirrup.

Dangling between the saddle and a very unpleasant landing, Lacey slid closer and closer to the ground. Still the horse rode on, refusing to stop or even slow down. Just as Lacey was about to panic, the grocery store manager ran to the wall behind her and pulled the plug.

Lacey slid to the tile floor. Safe, at last.

As for Thunderbolt, he didn't even give Lacey a second glance. He simply stood there. Motionless. Waiting for the next victim with a quarter in her hand…

It would be nice if the expectations in our head would line up with the reality in which we live. But sometimes, there's a disconnect. Marriage, parenting, a promotion at work, owning a horse…whatever it is that disappoints us (when we expected it to delight us) can plant a tiny seed of bitterness in our soul. The more we nurture that seed, the deeper the roots of resentment grow, until eventually they work their way into other areas of our lives.

That's why it's good to make certain the soil of our soul isn't primed to offer favorable conditions in which bitterness can grow. How can we do that? Let go of grudges. Do what we can to foster forgiveness. Refuse to play the blame game. Stop gossip before it starts. Admit to others and ourselves when we are part of the problem. Refuse to expect those we love to read our minds–clearly voice our expectations.

It's okay to dream. It helps us plan for the future. It gets our creative juices flowing. It strengthens our hearts by offering hope. We simply need to remind ourselves that expectations are just that: dreams. They're not guarantees.

It doesn't make sense to climb into the saddle expecting you're going to fall. That makes for

a tentative, uncomfortable ride. So, go ahead:
Expect the best. Just keep reality clearly in view.
Nurture honesty, flexibility and forgiveness.
Then, set your sights on the horizon and enjoy
the ride.

*I*t seems to me we can never give up longing
and wishing while we are thoroughly alive.
There are certain things we feel to be beautiful
and good, and we must hunger after them.

George Eliot

*I*f your dreams turn to dust…vacuum.

Author Unknown

*G*od's gifts put man's best dreams to shame.

Elizabeth Barrett Browning

*H*appy is the man who early learns the wide
chasm that lies between his wishes and his
powers.

Johann von Goethe

*N*obody has things just as he would like them.
The thing to do is to make a success with what
material I have. It is a sheer waste of time and
soul-power to imagine what I would do if things
were different. They are not different.

Dr. Frank Crane

THE SUNSHINE'S GOLDEN GLEAM IS THROWN
ON SORREL, CHESTNUT, BAY, AND ROAN;
THE HORSES PAW AND PRANCE AND NEIGH,
FILLIES AND COLTS LIKE KITTENS PLAY,
AND DANCE AND TOSS THEIR RIPPLED MANES
SHINING AND SOFT AS SILKEN SKEINS.

CARE, AND NOT FINE STABLES,
MAKES A GOOD HORSE.
PROVERB

Beginnings

From tender foal attempting to stand on her long, wobbly legs, to grand dame of pasture and field, a horse is one of nature's wonders. Just watching the antics of colts and fillies frolicking in the corral never fails to bring a smile. That's honest to goodness horseplay!

Those who know the art of teaching a young horse to trot and gallop, to prance and parade know the rewards of nurturing the talents, abilities, and intelligence of another living creature. Those who shelter and befriend, admire and love, enjoy and appreciate horses find in them a faithful and affectionate companion.

In later years of her cherished life the aged horse is drawn toward familiar pastures, enjoying the simple pleasures of sweet grass and a warm sun. She has seen many days, heard many voices, knows many things…her wisdom whispers in the depth of her soft brown eyes.

*A*nd whatsoever ye do, do it heartily, as to the Lord, and not unto men.

Colossians 3:23

*H*ave a purpose in life, and having it, throw into your work such strength of mind and muscle as God has given you.

Thomas Carlyle

*A*bout the head of a truly great horse there is an air of freedom unconquerable. The eyes seem to look on heights beyond our gaze. It is the look of a spirit that can soar.

John Taintor Foote

*T*he LORD is my strength and my shield; my heart trusted in him, and I am helped: therefore my heart greatly rejoiceth; and with my song will I praise him.

Psalm 28:7

WHAT IT'S REALLY ALL ABOUT...
IS LOVE.